WHOLE FOOD

HEALTHIER LIFESTYLE DIET

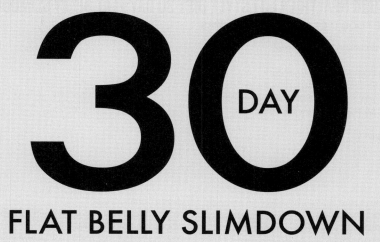

30 DAY

FLAT BELLY SLIMDOWN

THE WHOLE FOOD HEALTHIER LIFESTYLE DIET 30 DAY FLAT BELLY SLIMDOWN

OVER 70 WHOLE FOOD DIET COMPLIANT RECIPES

DISCLAIMER

CONTENTS

DINNER RECIPES

SNACKS

SMOOTHIES

INTRODUCTION

If we all stop just for a few seconds and pay attention to what our bodies are saying and respect that, only then will we understand that our bodies need real food to function and heal.

For many years, humans lived on the natural nutrients that nature provides us with, but over the last century food has changed dramatically. Both the production of food and the type of food we consume.

Today, it's increasingly harder to find an ingredient that has naturally grown under the sun without any artificial accelerants. Instead, the food industry giants are continually looking for cheaper ways of producing more and more food and in doing so they are altering the manner in which food is grown; moving further and further away from a natural non-interventionist approach.

WHAT DOES THIS MEAN FOR US?

The sad thing is that, as our schedules become tighter and tighter, most of us are opting for empty-calorie, ready-to-eat foods from these food giants that only need to be popped in the microwave for 3 minutes and voilà! Dinner is ready!

If we all stop just for a few seconds and pay attention to what our bodies are saying and respect that, only then will we understand that our bodies need real food to function and heal.

This is where the 30 Day Diet comes in; healthy living is a lifestyle and starting with the 30 Day Diet is the first step to success. When undertaking the 30 Day Diet, you should place emphasis on eating dark green leafy veggies, plant based foods and other natural foods that have undergone zero or minimal processing. This book gives you a broad outline of the principles of the 30 Day Diet along with over 70 healthy recipes to complement this approach.

The 30 Day Diet has gained increasing popularity and actually it's a lot simpler than you might expect. With a little determination, a little planning and our simple recipes, it's totally possible for anyone to incorporate into their lives Our delicious recipes are made using every day healthy ingredients so don't worry about spiralling costs. We'll keep things uncomplicated. Your health and well-being simply starts with food.
So, let's get started!

THE A,B,Cs OF THE 30 DAY DIET

As you get ready to embark on the journey, the first thing you need to understand is that your health, weight and overall well-being are all determined by what you eat. Everything starts with food!

Certain food groups (like dairy, grains, sugar, legumes and processed foods) could be having a negative impact on your overall health without you even noticing it. Now, the challenge is, how do you know if these foods are affecting you and how they are affecting you?

The answer is quite simple – strip them from your diet for a whole 30 days!

Cut out all the hormone unbalancing, inflammatory, and psychologically unhealthy and gut disrupting food groups for a month and give your body a fighting chance to recover and heal from all the effects these foods have been causing.

It's time to push the 'reset' button on your systemic inflammation, metabolism and all the downstream effects of the diet choices you've been making. It's time to learn, once and for all, how your food choices are actually affecting your daily life and your long-term health.

THE 30 DAY DIET RULES

Yes: Eat natural, real food

Eat tons of fresh vegetables, seafood, some fruit, meat, plenty of good fats from seeds, fruits, nuts, fatty fish like salmon and oils. Eat foods with very few ingredients or better yet, foods with no listed ingredients because they are in their pure and natural form.

No: Foods not to eat for 30 days

Most importantly, here's what to AVOID for the 30 days. Omitting all these foods will help you regain your energy, healthy metabolism and significantly reduce systemic inflammation whilst helping you to discover how these foods have been impacting your health, quality of life and fitness.

Stay away from sugar of all kinds (artificial or natural)

Don't take any alcohol (not even in your cooking)

Don't eat any grains or legumes

Don't eat any dairy

Don't take any MSG carrageenan or sulphites (check your food labels)

Don't try to recreate treats, baked foods or junk foods with the approved ingredients

Exceptions to the rule:

The following foods are allowed:

Fresh fruit juice as a sweetener

Ghee

Vinegar

Certain legumes such as snow peas, green beans and sugar snap peas due to the fact that they are more 'pod' and green matter than 'grain'.

Sparing use of salt

THE HEALTH BENEFITS

Increased fibre intake: The 30 Day Diet places greater emphasis on fruit and veggies, which are naturally endowed with fibre. Fibre plays an important role in your body by binding to toxins and eliminating them through waste and also improving your digestive function. Some of the foods which are rich in fibre are almonds, broccoli, and citrus fruit.

Break the unhealthy chain of food addiction: "I had a terrible day, I need my favourite pick-me-up (ice cream) to cheer me up!" Does this sound like you? Well, you can say goodbye, once and for all, to your terrible food addictions and obsessions.
The 30 Day Diet rewires your entire system and reminds every single organ in your body that it needs healthy and natural food to provide it with first-grade fuel, not empty calorie foods.

Manage and reverse symptoms of chronic illnesses: The reason why western medicine sometimes fails is because it only focuses on healing the symptoms and not the disease itself. A good example of this is; you are suffering from a food sensitivity, on seeing your GP, you may be prescribed medication to reduce the discomfort of the inflammation. The problem with this approach is that it does not address the underlying cause of inflammation. What triggered your immune system to respond with inflammation that manifested as a food sensitivity in the first place? More often than not the problem and the cure begins with food!
The diet is comprised of the purest foods that help your body trigger its self-healing ability to help combat even the most serious of health conditions.

Having a problem with your reproductive function?: The typical Western diet is laden with artificial ingredients that are doused with chemicals, some of which mimic the hormone estrogen. For women, the body is fooled into thinking that there is enough estrogen and so it withholds itself from releasing estrogen therein affecting fertility. Ever seen men with boobs (moobs), this is because the estrogen-mimicking chemicals cause the men to have a higher level of 'estrogen' than they should have and as a result have lower testosterone levels.
The 30 Day Diet aims to detoxify and reboot your entire system, thus restoring normalcy in your endocrine function.

Discover the fountain of youth: You will be surprised at how clear and radiant your skin can look after 30 days of no junk food; and not just your skin but also hair and nails.
Your skin is a mirror of how healthy you are. By cutting out all processed foods, your skin should begin to improve and express your improved healthy state.

No more sleepless nights: One of the most welcome benefits of this diet is that it regulates your hormone patterns meaning your body will stay awake when it should and completely shut down when it's supposed to; leading to a natural sleep pattern. As well as helping you feel refreshed after a good nights sleep, your body will use those sleeping hours to heal and repair damaged tissue.
With a healthy and nutritious 30 Day Diet you can expect a lot of sleeping, healing and repairing.

Enjoy full-blown and consistent energy: Forget about energy highs and lows of sugar and carb crashes. This diet offers you consistent energy release throughout the day.

Bid farewell to digestive distress: Forget about tummy rumbles and unending gas. You might have a little discomfort if your previous diet did not feature lots of veggies, but after that, it should be smooth sailing.

Know the difference between real hunger and emotional appetite: You will be familiar with the mindless eating that happens when you are under emotional stress. This emotional appetite and usually craves junk food. With the 30 Day Diet your body will be weaned off the sugar spikes and should settle into proper insulin management, your appetite will start diminishing and real hunger – the need for nutritious food, will clearly signal to you when to eat.

Find new favourite foods: There's so much room on your plate and in your kitchen for new tastes now that all the junk food is out and who knows which spices, veggies, fruits and meats will become your new favourites?

COUNTING CALORIES?

The 30 Day Diet has been designed as an elimination diet that is focused on you as an individual; helping you feel your absolute best.

It is not a weigh loss plan. There is no calorie counting but many people do end up losing weight as a result of cutting out sugar and losing the empty calories from desserts, baked goods, and alcohol. Chances are you'll also find that your belly feels flatter as a result of avoiding highly processed packaged foods, which tend to be loaded with sodium.

Don't concentrate on calories. Concentrate on the goodness of the food you are eating and rather than a daily 'weigh-in', only step on the scales at the start and the end of the program if you want to check on your weight loss. The 30 Day Diet approach focuses on how your body feels and on building a new healthy relationship with food. It's not centred purely on what the scales say.

30 DAY

FLAT BELLY SLIMDOWN

BREAKFAST
RECIPES

THREE BERRY & SEED PARFAIT

Ingredients

- 2 tsp fresh lemon juice
- 2 tbsp fresh pineapple juice
- 500ml/2 cups coconut yogurt
- 250g/9oz fresh sliced strawberries
- 250g/9oz fresh blueberries

- 250g/9oz fresh raspberries
- 1 tbsp hemp seeds
- 1 tbsp chia seeds
- 1 tbsp ground flax seeds

Method

1 In a small bowl, combine together the fresh lemon juice, pineapple juice and yogurt. Stir until the mixture is well blended.

2 Lay out 4 tall parfait glasses. Carefully add a layer of the yogurt mixture & top with berries and seeds. to each glass.

3 Repeat the layers until all the ingredients are used up.

CHEF'S NOTE

Lemon juice is a wonderful source of Vitamin C; it contains antioxidants and helps strengthen your veins; citric acid and pectin help prevent hunger and it encourages the body to burn fat. Replace lemon juice with fresh lime or orange juice. Serve sprinkled with more seeds.

SPICED MEXICAN BREAKFAST SCRAMBLE

SERVES 2

30 DAY
FLAT BELLY SLIMDOWN

Ingredients

- 1 tbsp coconut oil
- ¼ red onion, diced
- ¼ green pepper, diced
- 1 tbsp hot sauce
- 4 free-range eggs

- ½ tsp red pepper flakes, crushed
- ½ tsp cumin
- Pinch of sea salt
- Pinch of pepper
- 2 tbsp freshly prepared salsa

Method

1 Melt coconut oil in a nonstick frying pan set over medium heat.

2 Stir in rthe ed onions and peppers and sauté for about 4 minutes or until onions are translucent.

3 Meanwhile, in a bowl, whisk together the hot sauce, eggs, crushed red pepper flakes, cumin, salt and peppers until frothy; add to onion mixture and cook, stirring, until eggs are set.

4 Season with salt and pepper and top with salsa.

5 Serve immediately.

CHEF'S NOTE

Start off your day with these unforgettable eggs that are wonderfully tasty. Low in carbs, high in protein, they make an effective fat burning breakfast or brunch meal that is very satisfying.

BERRY DANDELION SMOOTHIE

SERVES 1

30 DAY
FLAT BELLY SLIMDOWN

Ingredients

- 250g/9oz fresh blueberries
- 250g/9oz fresh cherries, pitted
- 2 medjool dates, pitted

- 1 tbsp flaxseeds
- ½ a bunch fresh dandelion
- 125ml/ ½ cup coconut water

Method

1 In your blender, combine blueberries, cherries, and dates.

2 Blend for 30 seconds and then add flaxseeds, dandelion and coconut water.

3 Blend the ingredients until very smooth.

4 Refrigerate until chilled before serving.

CHEF'S NOTE

Whip up this healthy smoothie three times a week for a grounding, energizing, and hormone balancing treat. Flaxseeds are packed full of nutrients; this essential fatty acid helps to reduce the amount of 'bad' cholesterol in the bloodstream and prevent blood clots and may also improve mood and alleviate depression.

COCONUT GREEN SMOOTHIE

Ingredients

- 500g/18oz fresh baby spinach, chopped
- 500ml/2 cups organic coconut milk, unsweetened
- 125g/4oz fresh mint, chopped
- 4 pitted medjool dates

- 2 medium bananas, chopped
- 1 tsp pure vanilla extract

Optional toppings:
- Cacao nibs
- Fresh cherries

Method

1 Combine the coconut milk, spinach and mint leaves in your blender and process until very smooth.

2 Add in all the remaining smoothie ingredients. Continue blending until you achieve your desired consistency.

3 Serve in a tall glass and top with your favourite toppings. Enjoy!

CHEF'S NOTE

This super healthy smoothie is packed with hormone-balancing goodness! Spinach is an excellent antioxidant and a great source of vitamin K. Spinach is extremely heart-friendly, thanks to its high folate content and its high fibre content helps keep your bowels regular.

CHIA SEED LIME MANGO PUDDING

Ingredients

- 750g/1lb 9oz fresh mango chunks
- 500ml/2 cups coconut milk
- 60ml/¼ cup freshly squeezed lime juice
- 1 tbsp lime zest
- 60ml/¼ cup fresh pineapple juice
- 60g/2oz hemp seeds
- 125g/4oz chia seeds
- Mango, diced, for topping

Method

1 Blend together the mango chunks, coconut milk, lime juice, lime zest, and fresh pineapple until very smooth

2 Add the hemp and chia seeds to the blender.

3 Continue pulsing until you achieve the desired consistency.

4 Refrigerate for about 1 hour before serving.

CHEF'S NOTE

Enjoy this superfood breakfast experience which will help you get rid of those stubborn extra pounds thanks to antioxidant, fibre, protein and nutrient rich ingredients which will have your metabolism on overdrive.

HEALTHY GREEN CHIA PUDDING

30 DAY
FLAT BELLY SLIMDOWN

Ingredients

- 250g/9oz fresh spinach
- 250ml/1 cup almond milk
- 1 date, pitted
- 3 tbsp chia seeds

- 1 kiwi fruit, peeled & chopped
- 1 handful of blueberries
- 1 tbsp chopped almonds

Method

1 Blend together the spinach, milk and date until smooth.

2 Transfer the spinach mixture to a bowl and stir in chia seeds.

3 Server the chia pudding topped with the chopped kiwi, almonds and berries.

CHEF'S NOTE

Best served chilled. Enjoy our superfood breakfast experience that will help you get rid of those stubborn extra pounds thanks to antioxidant, fibre, protein and nutrient rich ingredients used to make this pudding that will have your metabolism on overdrive.

SPICY BREAKFAST PORRIDGE

SERVES 5

30 DAY

FLAT BELLY SLIMDOWN

Ingredients

- 500ml/2 cups coconut milk
- 2 ripe bananas, mashed
- 60g/2½oz flax meal
- 175g/6oz almond meal
- Pinch of ground nutmeg

- Pinch of ground cloves
- ½ tsp ginger
- 1 tsp cinnamon
- Pinch of sea salt

Method

1 Place a medium-sized saucepan over a medium to low heat.

2 Add the coconut milk, mashed bananas, flax meal, almond meal, nutmeg, cloves, ginger, cinnamon and salt.

3 Simmer, stirring, until thick and bubbly.

4 Remove from heat and serve hot.

CHEF'S NOTE

Try serving this porridge topped with some toasted coconut flakes and a handful of blueberries. Blueberries are rich in antioxidants and they help reduce inflammation.

CHIA SEED & PEANUT BUTTER PUDDING

Ingredients

- 125g4 oz natural peanut butter
- 375ml/1½ cups almond milk
- 2 very ripe bananas

- 3 tbsp chia seeds
- 3 tbsp flaxseeds

Method

1 Add the peanut butter, almond milk, and peeled bananas to a blender.

2 Process until very smooth and pour into a large bowl.

3 Stir in chia seeds and flax seeds and then divide among the serving bowls.

4 Refrigerate the pudding for at least 4 hours before serving - when ready, stir and serve topped with more seeds.

CHEF'S NOTE

Chia seeds are high in quality protein and deliver a massive amount of nutrients with very few calories..

SPICY HEALTHY SALMON FRITTATA

30 DAY

FLAT BELLY SLIMDOWN

Ingredients

- 1 tbsp coconut oil
- 1 red onion, chopped
- 1 green pepper, chopped
- 2 garlic cloves, minced
- 375g/13oz cherry tomatoes
- ½ tsp paprika

- 1 tsp cumin
- 125g/4oz cooked salmon flakes
- 6 free-range eggs beaten
- Pinch of sea salt
- Pinch of pepper
- 2 tbsp chopped coriander

Method

1 Preheat oven to 180°C/350°F/4 gas mark.

2 Melt the butter in an oven-safe frying pan and sauté the red onion and green pepper. Stir in garlic and cook for about 2 minutes.

3 Stir in the paprika, cumin, salt & pepper and cook for another minute; stir in tomatoes and cook until soft.

4 Sprinkle with salmon and cover with eggs; season with salt and pepper and bake for about 15 minutes or until the eggs are set.

5 Serve warm garnished with coriander.

CHEF'S NOTE

You can prepare this recipe the night before and reheat it in the morning. Freeze leftovers for later use.

DAIRY FREE RAINBOW ACAI BOWL

30 DAY
FLAT BELLY SLIMDOWN

········· *Ingredients* ·········

- 60g/4oz frozen raspberries
- 60g/2½ oz frozen blueberries
- 125ml/½ cup coconut yoghurt
- 1 tsp chia seeds
- 1 tsp acai powder
- 1 mango, sliced

- 2 tbsp blueberries
- 2 strawberries, hulled, sliced
- ½ ripe banana, sliced
- 1 small orange, segmented
- 1 tbsp pistachios, chopped, toasted

········· *Method* ·········

1 In a blender, add together the berries, yogurt, chia seed, acai powder, and mango.

2 Blend the mixture until very smooth.

3 Spoon into two serving bowls and top each with fresh blueberries, strawberries, banana, orange and pistachios.

4 Enjoy!

CHEF'S NOTE

This is a fun breakfast/brunch for the whole family that's so easy to prepare. The recipe is very versatile and you can get experimenting with your favourite ingredients.

SWEET SUPERFOOD 'PORRIDGE'

30 DAY

FLAT BELLY SLIMDOWN

Ingredients

- 375ml/1½ cups almond milk
- Handful chopped almonds
- 2 tbsp ground flaxseed
- 3 tbsp chia seeds
- 3 tbsp shredded unsweetened coconut

- 1 tsp pure vanilla extract

Toppings:
- 3 tsp peanut butter
- 3 tsp toasted coconut flakes

Method

1 In a large bowl, mix all ingredients together except the topping ingredients.

2 Refrigerate, covered, overnight.

3 In the morning divide the 'porridge' into serving bowls.

4 Top each serving with peanut butter and toasted coconut.

5 Serve right away.

CHEF'S NOTE

Need to take a break from your regular oatmeal porridge? Our grain-free power porridge is the perfect substitute with healthy and slimming ingredients. Try substituting walnuts for almonds in this recipe.

HEALTHY SPICY PANCAKES

30 DAY
FLAT BELLY SLIMDOWN

Ingredients

- 4 tbsp coconut oil
- 250ml/1 cup coconut milk
- 125g/4oz tapioca flour
- 125ml/4oz almond flour
- 1 tsp salt
- ½ tsp chilli powder

- ¼ tsp turmeric powder
- ¼ tsp black pepper
- ½ inch ginger, grated
- 1 serrano pepper, minced
- 1 handful coriander, chopped
- ½ red onion, chopped

Method

1 In a bowl, combine the coconut milk, tapioca flour, almond flour and spices until well blended; stir in the ginger, Serrano pepper, coriander, and red onion until well combined.

2 Melt the coconut oil in a saucepan over medium low heat; add about ¼ cup/60g of batter and spread out on the pan.

3 Cook for 3-4 minutes per side or until golden brown.

4 Transfer to a plate and keep warm; repeat with the remaining batter and oil.

5 Serve the pancakes with freshly squeezed orange juice.

CHEF'S NOTE

Try crushing one clove of garlic and combine it with some tahini sauce. Thin it with a splash of fresh lemon juice then serve with the pancakes.

DELICIOUS BREAKFAST TURKEY CASSEROLE

30 DAY
FLAT BELLY SLIMDOWN

Ingredients

- 1 tbsp coconut oil
- 500g/18oz minced turkey
- 1 large sweet potato, cut into slices
- 1250g/4oz spinach
- 12 eggs
- Salt and pepper

Method

1 Preheat the oven to 180°C/350°F/4 gas mark.

2 Lightly coat a square baking tray with coconut oil and set aside.

3 In a frying pan set over a medium heat brown the minced turkey in coconut oil; season well and remove from heat.

4 Layer the potato slices onto the baking tray and top with the spinach and turkey mince.

5 In a small bowl, whisk eggs, salt and pepper until well blended; pour over the mixture to cover completely.

6 Bake for about 45 minutes or until the eggs are cooked through and the potatoes are tender.

CHEF'S NOTE

Replace ground turkey with ground chicken if you prefer.

VEGETABLE BREAKFAST CASSEROLE

30 DAY

FLAT BELLY SLIMDOWN

······ *Ingredients* ······

- 250g/9oz bacon, chopped
- 250g/9oz red onion, diced
- 250g/9oz carrots, shredded
- 250g/9oz diced green pepper
- 500g/18oz chopped courgette

- 750g/27oz spinach
- 250ml/1 cup water
- 12 free-range eggs, beaten
- 1 tsp sea salt
- ½ tsp pepper

······ *Method* ······

1 Preheat the oven to 180°C/350°F/4 gas mark.

2 Coat a 9x13-inch casserole dish with olive oil cooking spray and set aside.

3 Cook the bacon in a frying pan over a medium heat for about 10 minutes or until crispy; stir in the red onions, carrots, green pepper & courgette and continue cooking for about 5 minutes or until the veggies are tender.

4 Stir in the spinach and cook for 2 minutes or until wilted; remove from heat.

5 In a seperate bowl mix together the water, eggs and salt until well combined.

6 Transfer the vegetable mixture to the casserole dish and cover with the egg mixture; stir well and bake for about 40-60 minutes or until eggs are set.

CHEF'S NOTE

You can use all kinds of ingredients in this dish –add jarred red peppers, minced garlic or any leftover veggies.

SWEET & SAVORY BREAKFAST SALAD

30 DAY
FLAT BELLY SLIMDOWN

······· *Ingredients* ·······

- 2 tbsp toasted sesame oil
- 1 green pepper, diced

- 250g/9oz diced pineapple
- 2 tbsp fresh lime juice

······· *Method* ·······

1 Place a frying pan over medium heat.

2 When hot, add sesame oil and heat until hot but not smoky.

3 Sauté the peppers and pineapple until tender and lightly browned.

4 Stir in fresh lime juice and remove from heat.

5 Serve right away.

CHEF'S NOTE

Pineapple contains antioxidants that get rid of free radicals, keeping you young and healthy. Replace lime juice with freshly squeezed lemon or orange juice.

GRAIN-FREE MUESLI

30 DAY

FLAT BELLY SLIMDOWN

Ingredients

- 125g/4oz unsweetened coconut flakes
- 125g/4oz mixed dried fruit (apple, cranberry, and apricot)
- 750g1lb 11oz mixed seeds (pumpkin, sunflower, chia, and hemp)

- 125ml/½ cup non-dairy milk (coconut, almond, cashew, or hemp)
- 1 banana, sliced
- 125g/4oz fresh berries (raspberries, blueberries, or strawberries)

Method

1 In a large bowl, combine together the coconut flakes, dried fruit, and mixed seeds.

2 Stir in the milk until well combined.

3 Divide themuesli among serving bowls.

4 Top each serving with sliced banana and fresh berries.

5 Enjoy!

CHEF'S NOTE
Bananas have much to offer when it comes to balancing hormones; they can help with weight control and high blood pressure.

27

AVOCADO SUPERFOOD TAPENADE & EGG TOAST

30 DAY
FLAT BELLY SLIMDOWN

Ingredients

- 4 gluten-free toasts
- 2 tsp tahini
- 1 ripe avocado, peeled and cut into slices
- 2 free-range eggs, poached
- 2 tsp chia seeds

- 2 tsp pumpkin seeds
- 2 tbsp superfood tapenade
For the tapenade
- 2 tsp extra virgin olive oil
- 1 tbsp lemon juice
- 1 garlic clove

- ½ tsp spirulina
- 1 tsp pumpkin seeds
- 125g/4oz green pitted olives
- 250g/9ozfresh kale leaves
- A pinch sea salt

Method

1 Drizzle the tahini sauce over the toasts and add the avocado slices.

2 Top with with poached eggs.

3 In a blender, pulse the tapenade ingredients until very smooth and store in an airtight container.

4 Add two tbsp of the tapenade over the toast and garnish with chia and pumpkin seeds. Serve right away.

CHEF'S NOTE

This breakfast toast recipe is gluten-free and features health-giving ingredients such as lemon juice, spriluna, and tahini. Lemon juice is a wonderful source of Vitamin C; it contains antioxidants and helps strengthen veins and prevents fluid retention; citric acid and pectin help prevent hunger and it encourages the body to burn fat. Spirulina is one of the most powerful hormone-balancing superfoods. Spinach is an excellent antioxidant and a great source of vitamin K.

SPINACH MANGO BREAKFAST SMOOTHIE

30 DAY
FLAT BELLY SLIMDOWN

Ingredients

- 125g/4oz fresh coriander, roughly chopped
- 375g/13oz fresh spinach, roughly chopped
- 500ml/2 cups chilled coconut water
- 250g/9oz frozen pineapple chunks
- 250g/9oz frozen mango chunks
- ½ an avocado, chopped
- 1 scoop (30g) protein powder

Method

1 Combine the chopped coriander, spinach and water in your blender and pulse three times. Add in the pineapple, mango and avocado.

2 Continue pulsing until you attain a smooth consistency.

3 Serve in tall glasses.

4 Enjoy!

CHEF'S NOTE

This sweet and sassy cleansing smoothie is loaded up with spinach, sweet tropical fruit, and chilled coconut water to help your body flush out toxins and balance hormones. Coconut water is packed with antioxidants that get rid of free radicals from the body and it also helps moisturize the body from within.

POACHED EGGS OVER MUSHROOMS & SPINACH

SERVES 3

30 DAY
FLAT BELLY SLIMDOWN

Ingredients

- 3 free-range eggs
- 500g/18oz spinach, thawed
- 3 medium cloves garlic
- 1 medium tomato, chopped
- 500g/18oz chopped crimini mushrooms

- ½ medium onion
- 1 tbsp vegetable or broth
- 1 tsp light vinegar
- Salt
- Pepper

Method

1 Chop the garlic & onion.

2 In the meantime, bring water to a rolling boil in a frying pan.

3 Add a tsp of vinegar.

4 Heat broth in a separate frying pan and stir in mushrooms and onion and cook for about 3 minutes over medium heat.

5 Stir in spinach, garlic, tomato, pepper and salt and cook for 3-5 more minutes.

6 Meanwhile add the eggs to the boiling water and poach for at least 5 minutes.

7 Plate up the spinach and mushroom mixture.

8 Remove the eggs from the boiling water and serve over the spinach mixture.

CHEF'S NOTE
Spinach is an excellent source of vitamin K and is extremely heart-friendly, thanks to its high folate levels, and its high fibre content helps keep your bowels regular.

30 DAY

DAY

FLAT BELLY SLIMDOWN

LUNCH
RECIPES

SALMON & GREENS SALAD WITH TOASTED WALNUTS

30 DAY
FLAT BELLY SLIMDOWN

Ingredients

- 1 tbsp extra-virgin olive oil
- 1kg/2¼ mixed salad greens (rocket, spinach, cos lettuce)
- 2 tbsp chopped toasted walnuts

- 1 tsp walnut oil
- ¼ tsp sea salt
- 350g/2oz salmon fillet
- Mustard salad spray

Method

1 Preheat a grill.

2 In a dry frying pan set over medium heat, toast the walnuts for about 1 minute and transfer to a plate.

3 Add half of the extra virgin olive oil to the same frying pan and sauté half of the greens for about 1 minute; transfer to a salad bowl and repeat with the remaining oil and greens. Add the salt to the and toss until well combined.

4 Brush the salmon with a little oil and grill the for about 10 minutes or until cooked through.

5 Cut into 4 pieces; divide the green salad among four serving bowls and top each with one piece of fish.

CHEF'S NOTE

You can add a salad dressing to this salad. However, avoid the store bought dressings as they usually contain a lot of sugar and oil. You can instead make a simple vinaigrette by combining olive oil, mustard and vinegar. Whisk them together and drizzle over your salad.

LEMONY GREEN SOUP WITH CAYENNE

30 DAY
FLAT BELLY SLIMDOWN

Ingredients

- 500g/18oz curly kale, torn
- 250g/4oz baby spinach
- 2 yellow onions, chopped
- 2 tbsp olive oil

- 1 litre/4 cups homemade vegetable stock
- 1 tbsp fresh lemon juice
- 1 large pinch of cayenne pepper
- Salt, to taste

Method

1 Add the two tbsp of olive oil in a large pan and cook the onions over medium heat.

2 Sprinkle with salt and cook for 5 minutes until they start browning.

3 Lower the heat and pour in two tbsp of water.

4 Cover, lower the heat and cook for 25 minutes until the onions caramelize, stirring frequently.

5 Steam kale for about 5 minutes or until wilted.

6 Add in the onions to the together with the broth, spinach and cayenne and simmer for 5 minutes.

7 Use an immersion blender to puree the rice mixture until smooth then stir in the lemon juice.

8 Serve into soup bowls and drizzle each with some olive oil.

CHEF'S NOTE

This soup is not only comforting but it is made with fat burning ingredients. It is loaded with red onions, green peppers, garlic and just the right amount of spices.

ROCKET SALAD WITH FRUIT & CHICKEN

SERVES 1

30 DAY
FLAT BELLY SLIMDOWN

Ingredients

- 1 tbsp extra-virgin olive oil
- 100g/3 ½oz chicken
- 200g/7oz rocket
- 1 tbsp chopped red onion

- Strawberry, apple, grapefruit or orange slices
- Pinch of salt & pepper
- Your favourite dressing

Method

1 Heat olive oil in a frying pan until hot but not smoky.

2 Add the chicken and cook until browned on both sides.

3 In a large bowl, combine rocket, fruit and chopped red onion.

4 Sprinkle the rocket salad with salt and pepper.

5 Place the sliced chicken on the rocket salad.

6 Top with fruit and drizzle with dressing & serve right away.

CHEF'S NOTE
You can replace chicken with beef or turkey. Drain off excess grease after browning your meat before adding other ingredients for an oily free dish.

MIXED SALAD WITH RASPBERRY VINAIGRETTE

SERVES 4

30 DAY
FLAT BELLY SLIMDOWN

Ingredients

- 250g/9oz microgreens
- 250g/9oz mixed greens
- ½ cooking apple, peeled & chopped
- ½ small cucumber, thinly sliced
- 3 carrots, sliced
- 1 tbsp sherry vinegar

- 2 tbsp extra virgin olive oil
- 1 tbsp mustard
- 2 raspberries, chopped
- 4 hardboiled eggs
- Pinch of sea salt
- Pinch of pepper

Method

1 In a large bowl, combine the microgreens, mixed greens, apple, cucumber, and carrots.

2 Combine together the sherry vinegar, olive oil, mustard, raspberries, salt and pepper in a sealable jar to make a dressing.

3 Shake the dressing vigorously to combine well.

4 Pour over the salad and toss to coat well.

5 Serve on plates topped with chopped hardboiled egg.

CHEF'S NOTE

Microgreens are the shoots of salad vegetables such as rocket, celery, beetroot, etc., picked just after the first leaves have developed.

INSTANT POT COCONUT CABBAGE

SERVES 4

30 DAY
FLAT BELLY SLIMDOWN

Ingredients

- 2 tbsp olive oil
- 2 tbsp lemon juice
- 1 medium carrot, sliced
- 1 medium brown onion, sliced
- 1 medium cabbage, shredded
- 1 tbsp turmeric powder
- 1 tbsp mild curry powder
- 1 tsp mustard powder
- ½ long red chilli, sliced
- 2 large cloves of garlic, diced
- 1 + ½ tsp salt
- 125ml/½ coconut milk

Method

1 Heat a frying pan on medium heat along with the oilve oil.

2 Stir in the onion and salt and cook for about 4 minutes.

3 Stir in the spices, chilli and garlic for about 30 seconds. Stir in the remaining ingredients and cover.

4 Cook for about 5 minutes and then remove from heat.

5 Serve hot.

CHEF'S NOTE
Here's a twist on your typical cabbage dish. This cabbage dish is made with healthy full fat coconut milk and spices for a tasty and healthy meal to help you achieve your goal of losing weight.

HOT & SOUR THAI PRAWN SOUP

Ingredients

- 100g/3½ oz prawns, chopped
- 500ml/2 cups vegetable stock
- Juice of ½ lemon with rind
- 1 lemon grass stalk
- 2-3 slices of fresh ginger

- Pinch of red pepper flakes
- 1 onion, chopped
- 1 tbsp fresh chopped coriander
- Salt and pepper

Method

1 Add the stock to a saucepan and bring to a rolling boil.

2 Stir in onion, lemon juice, lemongrass, ginger and pepper and simmer for about 10-15 minutes.

3 Stir in prawns and coriander and continue cooking for 8 minutes more.

4 Remove the lemongrass. and serve hot.

CHEF'S NOTE
Coriander is excellent for the digestive system and nervous system; it's rich in iron and great for the skin

SWEET KALE & CRANBERRY SALAD

Ingredients

- 2 large peeled sweet potatoes, cubed
- 2 bunches kale, chopped into small pieces
- 1 tbsp fresh lemon juice
- 3 tbsp extra-virgin olive oil

- 4 tbsp sunflower seeds
- 125g/4oz dried cranberries
- 1 tsp Dijon mustard
- A pinch of sea salt
- A pinch of freshly ground pepper

Method

1 Place the potatoes in a medium saucepan and cover with water.

2 Stir in a pinch of salt and bring to a gentle boil.

3 Lower the heat to a simmer and simmer for about 15 minutes or until the potatoes are tender; drain and let cool.

4 In a large bowl, whisk together mustard, lemon juice and extra virgin olive oil.

5 Add the cooked sweet potatoes along with all the remaining ingredients.

6 Toss to mix well and serve.

CHEF'S NOTE
Substitute freshly squeezed orange or lime juice for lemon juice and baby spinach for kale.

COCONUT MILK MUSHROOM SOUP

30 DAY
FLAT BELLY SLIMDOWN

Ingredients

- 1 tbsp olive oil
- 750g/1lb 11oz mushrooms
- 1 clove garlic, minced
- 2 red onions, chopped
- 1 litre/4 cups vegetable stock
- 500ml/2 cups coconut milk
- 1 tbsp fresh thyme
- ⅛ tsp sea salt
- Thyme sprigs
- ⅛ tsp pepper

Method

1 Heat the oil and sauté the red onion and mushrooms in a soup pot for a few minutes.

2 Stir in vegetable stock and cook for 5 minutes.

3 Place about half the mixture into a blender and blend.

4 Add the coconut milk, garlic, and thyme and continue blending until very smooth and creamy.

5 Return the blended soup to the soup pot and season with salt, thyme sprigs and pepper to serve.

CHEF'S NOTE

A squeeze of fresh lime or lemon juice and a sprinkle of coarse sea salt and freshly ground pepper will add fresh flavour to this soup. You can refrigerate the soup for a few days.

SPICY CHICKEN SALAD

SERVES 4

Ingredients

- 1 tsp apple-cider vinegar
- ½ lemon, juiced
- 1 avocado, mashed
- 1 garlic cloves crushed
- 1 tsp powdered ginger

- 2 tsp powdered turmeric
- ¼ tsp sea salt
- 500g/1lb 2oz shredded cooked chicken breast
- 62 tbsp raisins
- 1 red onion, finely sliced

Method

1 In a bowl, mix together lemon juice, apple cider vinegar, avocado, garlic and ginger.

2 Sprinkle with turmeric and sea salt.

3 Add the shredded chicken, raisins, and red onion.

4 Stir to mix well.

CHEF'S NOTE
Substitute turkey or even beef for chicken breast. You can also use chicken wings instead of chicken breasts. Serve garnished with chopped fresh parsley.

BUTTERNUT SQUASH & COURGETTE NOODLES

Ingredients

- 3 large courgettes, julienned into noodles
- 750g/1lb 11oz cubed butternut squash
- 2 cloves garlic, finely chopped
- 1 onion, chopped
- 2 tbsp olive oil
- 500ml/2 cups homemade vegetable stock
- ¼ tsp red pepper flakes
- Freshly ground black pepper
- 1 tbsp fresh sage, finely chopped
- Salt, to taste

Method

1 Add the oil to a pan on medium heat and sauté the sage once it's hot until it turns crisp. Transfer to a small bowl and season lightly with salt ,then set aside.

2 Add the onion, squash, garlic and pepper flakes to the pan and cook for 8-10 minutes. Season with salt and pepper and pour in the broth.

3 Bring to a boil then simmer for 20 minutes until the butternut is tender.

4 Meanwhile, steam the courgette noodles in your microwave or steamer.

5 Once the butternut mixture is ready, remove from heat and let cool off slightly then transfer to a blender and process until smooth.

6 Combine the courgette noodles and the butternut puree in the frying pan over medium heat and cook until heated through and evenly coated.

7 Sprinkle with fried sage and serve hot.

CHEF'S NOTE
Add a pinch of cayenne pepper for a spicier dish.

CLEANSING SALAD WITH CITRUS DRESSING

30 DAY

FLAT BELLY SLIMDOWN

Ingredients

For salad
- 500g/2 cups red cabbage
- 500g/18oz kale, finely sliced
- 250g/9 oz parsley, chopped
- 1 red pepper, diced
- 250g/9oz radish
- 500g/18oz broccoli

- 250g/9oz carrots
- 250g/9oz raw walnuts, chopped
- 2 avocados, peeled and diced
- 2 tbsp sesame seeds
- freshly ground black pepper to taste

- For dressing
- 125ml/4floz fresh lemon juice
- 125ml/4floz fresh orange juice
- 125ml/4floz extra-virgin olive oil
- 1 tsp minced ginger
- Pinch of cayenne
- ¼ tsp sea salt

Method

1 Finely slice the cabbage and chop the broccoli..

2 Slice the radishes and carrots into matchsticks.

3 Combine all the dressing ingredients in a jar and shake well.

4 Combine the salad ingredients in a salad bowl.

5 Pour the dressing over the salad. Toss to combine well and serve

CHEF'S NOTE
This salad is made with nutrient-dense ingredients which help lower cholesterol and supercharge the immune system.

SERVES 2

LEMONY SPINACH & CHICKEN SOUP

Ingredients

- 1 tsp extra-virgin olive oil
- 100g/3½oz chicken
- 1 clove garlic, minced
- 1 tbsp chopped red onion
- ½ lemon with rind
- 1 stalk lemongrass

- ¼ tsp thyme
- Pinch of cayenne pepper
- Pinch of salt & pepper
- 500ml/2 cups chicken stock
- 60ml/¼ cup fresh lemon juice
- 500ml/18oz chopped spinach

Method

1 In a small saucepan brown the chicken in the olive oil.

2 Stir in the garlic, onion, herbs, spices, broth, lemon juice and lemon rind.

3 Simmer for about 20-30 minutes, adding spinach during the last 5 minutes.

4 Serve hot.

CHEF'S NOTE

This herb infused creamy soup packs a nutritional punch to keep you full until your next meal. It also helps melt stubborn fat away and keep it off the healthy way! Plus it's very yummy with a super fresh taste!

SHAVED VEGGIE SALAD WITH TOASTED SEEDS

SERVES 1

30 DAY
FLAT BELLY SLIMDOWN

Ingredients

- 250g/9oz spinach
- 2 radishes, thinly sliced
- 1 small yellow squash, thinly sliced
- 1 small beetroot, thinly sliced
- 1 small cucumber, thinly sliced
- 1 small carrot, thinly sliced
- 1 tbsp toasted pumpkin seeds
- 1 tbsp extra-virgin olive oil
- 1 lemon, juiced
- sea salt, to taste
- ground pepper, to taste

Method

1 Combine the veggies and greens in a large bowl.

2 Add the lemon juice and olive oil.

3 Toss until everything is well coated.

4 Season with salt and pepper and serve right away.

CHEF'S NOTE

You can replace squash with sweet potato and lemon juice with grapefruit or orange juice.

RAW VEGGIE RIBBON SALAD

Ingredients

- 2 medium courgette, thinly sliced
- 2 medium carrots, thinly sliced
- 5 asparagus spears, thinly sliced
- 2 tbsp sliced red onion
- 60ml/¼ cup balsamic vinaigrette

Method

1 In a large bowl, mix the courgettes, carrots, asparagus and onions together.

2 Drizzle each with vinaigrette and toss until well coated.

3 Serve right away.

4 Enjoy!

CHEF'S NOTE

Serve the salad topped with a handful of chopped Kalamata olives and grape tomatoes.

CLEANSING DETOX SOUP

30 DAY

FLAT BELLY SLIMDOWN

Ingredients

- 60ml/¼ cup water
- 2 cloves garlic, minced
- ½ of a red onion, diced
- 1 tbsp fresh ginger, peeled and minced
- 250g/9oz chopped tomatoes
- 1 small head of broccoli, florets

- 3 medium carrots, diced
- 3 celery stalks, diced
- 1 ½ litres/6 cups water
- ¼ tsp cinnamon
- 1 tsp turmeric
- ⅛ tsp chilli powder
- Sea salt

- Freshly ground black pepper
- juice of 1 lemon
- 1 handful cabbage, chopped
- 500g/18oz kale, torn in pieces

Method

1 Bring a large pot of water to a gentle boil over medium heat.

2 Add the garlic & onion and cook for about 2 minutes, stirring occasionally.

3 Stir in fresh ginger, tomatoes, broccoli, carrots, and celery and continue cooking for 3 minutes more.

4 Stir in cinnamon, chilli powder, turmeric, sea salt and black pepper.

5 Add in ½ cup/120ml water and bring the mixture to a rolling boil; reduce heat and simmer for about 15 minutes or until the veggies and tender.

6 Stir in the lemon juice, cabbage, and kale during the last 2 minutes of cooking.

7 Transfer to an immersion blender and blend until smooth.

8 Serve hot or warm.

CHEF'S NOTE

Add a pinch of cayenne pepper for a hot and better taste. In case you do not have an immersion blender, transfer the contents to your food processor and puree until smooth.

GREEN SUPER DETOX SALAD

Ingredients

- 1 tbsp extra virgin olive oil
- Juice from 1 lemon
- ½ avocado
- 2 large cucumbers
- ¼ cabbage

- 60g/2½ oz chopped celery
- 25g/1oz pistachios
- ¼ head broccoli
- Sea salt and pepper

Method

1 In a large bowl, combine extra virgin olive oil, lemon juice and avocado.

2 Mash with a fork until smooth and season with salt and pepper; set aside.

3 Using a spiralizer or a veggie peeler, turn the cucumber into 'noodles'.

4 Chop the remaining ingredients and toss them in a bowl with the cucumber noodles.

5 Add the avocado dressing and toss to combine well.

CHEF'S NOTE

Avocado is rich in heart-healthy fat while broccoli is low in calories and packed with a huge range of nutrients such as vitamin C, K and calcium.

GREEN SALAD & DETOX DRESSING

Ingredients

- For the salad:
- 100g /3½oz baby rocket
- 1 bunch salad onions, sliced
- ½ cucumber, thinly sliced
- 1 large carrot, shredded
- ½ medium beetroot, thinly shredded

- 1 firm ripe avocado, diced
- 2 tbsp raw sliced almonds
- 2 tbsp raw pumpkin seeds
- 2 tbsp sunflower seeds
- For the detox dressing:
- Juice of 2 lemons
- 125ml/ ½ cup avocado oil

- Pinch sea salt
- Pinch dry mustard powder
- Pinch black pepper
- 2 tbsp chopped parsley

Method

1 **Make the salad:** Toss rocket with sliced and shredded veggies in a large bowl.

2 Sprinkle with seeds and nuts and set aside.

3 **Make the Dressing:** Add the lemon juice to a jar along with the avocado oil, salt, mustard powder, and pepper.

4 Fit the lid and shake vigorously until well blended.

5 Add the parsley and continue shaking to mix well.

6 Pour the dressing over the salad and toss to coat well. Serve immediately.

CHEF'S NOTE

You can use toasted sesame oil instead of avocado oil in preparing the dressing for this salad.

BROCCOLI DETOX SOUP

SERVES 2

30 DAY

FLAT BELLY SLIMDOWN

Ingredients

- 1 tsp coconut oil
- 2 garlic cloves, crushed
- 1 onion, diced
- 500g/18oz broccoli florets
- 1 carrot, chopped
- 1 parsnip, chopped

- 2 celery stalks, diced
- 2 cups filtered water
- 250g/9oz greens (spinach, kale, or any other available)
- Juice of ½ lemon
- 1 tbsp chia seeds

- ½ tsp sea salt
- 1 tsp coconut milk, to serve
- Toasted mixed seeds and nuts, to serve

Method

1 Heat the coconut oil in a soup pot set over low heat; stir in garlic, onion, broccoli, celery sticks, parsnip, and carrot.

2 Cook for about 5 minutes, stirring frequently.

3 Stir in the water and bring the mixture to a gentle boil.

4 Cover and simmer for about 7 minutes or until veggies are tender.

5 Stir in the greens and transfer to a food processor or blender; add lemon juice, chia seeds, and sea salt and pulse until very smooth.

6 Stir in coconut milk and sprinkle with toasted seeds and serve right away.

CHEF'S NOTE

This comforting soup uses fresh vegetables which will provide you with the proper nourishment as you strive to reboot your system.

CARROT AND GOJI BERRY SOUP

Ingredients

- 310ml/1 ¼ cups fresh carrot juice
- 1 inch ginger,
- ½ inch turmeric
- 250g/9oz carrots, chopped
- 250g/9oz pumpkin
- 2 tbsp Goji berries
- 2 tbsp coconut oil

- 1 cup onion, chopped
- 1 red jalapeno pepper-seeds removed
- 500ml/2 cups water
- 125ml/ ½ cup light coconut milk
- 1 clove garlic
- Sea salt and cracked black pepper to taste

Method

1 Add the turmeric and ginger to the carrot juice.

2 Soak the goji berries in the juice for roughly 20 minutes.

3 Heat the coconut oil in a pot and add the onions; sauté for about 4 minutes or until soft, and then add the jalapeno pepper and garlic cook for 1 minute more.

4 Stir in the chopped carrots and water and bring to a boil. Once boiling, reduce heat to a simmer and cook, covered, for about 20 minutes.

5 Cool slightly and transfer the mixture to the blender and add the coconut milk; blend to a thick puree.

6 Strain the goji berries from the carrot juice and set the berries aside.

7 Add the carrrot juice to the puree and continue pureeing until smooth.

8 Season with salt and pepper to taste.

9 To serve, garnish each bowl with some of the goji berries.

CHEF'S NOTE
Try mashing up avocado and combine it with finely chopped coriander, chilli and lime juice.Dollop this onto your hot soup for a creamy and healthy addition.

KALE SALAD WITH GRAPEFRUIT & AVOCADO

30 DAY
FLAT BELLY SLIMDOWN

Ingredients

- 2 tbsp fresh orange juice
- 1 tbsp fresh grapefruit juice
- 1 clove garlic, minced
- A pinch of sea salt
- A pinch of pepper
- 120ml/½ cup extra virgin olive oil

- 750g/1lb 11oz shredded kale leaves
- 1 avocado, sliced
- 1 pink grapefruit, sectioned
- 2 tbsp sunflower seeds, toasted

Method

1 Make the dressing in a small bowl by whisking together orange juice, grapefruit juice, garlic, salt and pepper; let sit for at least 10 minutes.

2 Gradually whisk in extra virgin olive oil and set aside.

3 Add kale to another bowl and drizzle with a splash of the dressing; massage for about 2 minutes and let sit until tender.

4 Divide kale among serving plates and top each serving with avocado and grapefruit.

5 Sprinkle with toasted sunflower seeds and drizzle generously with the dressing to serve.

CHEF'S NOTE

This salad is made with healthy ingredients such as dark-green kale, avocado and grapefruit to help you burn excess fat. It's so tasty that it will become your favourite go-to healthy vegetarian meal.

30 DAY

DAY

FLAT BELLY SLIMDOWN

DINNER
RECIPES

PAN-FRIED CHILLI BEEF WITH TOASTED CASHEWS

30 DAY
FLAT BELLY SLIMDOWN

Ingredients

- ½ tbsp extra-virgin olive oil
- 500g/1lb 2oz sliced lean beef
- 2 tsp red curry paste
- 2 tbsp fresh lime juice
- 2 tsp fish sauce

- 250g/9oz green capsicum peppers, diced
- 120ml/½ cup water
- 24 toasted cashews, chopped
- 1 tsp arrowroot

Method

1 Add the oil to a pan set over medium heat; add the beef and fry for a minute or so until it's just slightly pink inside.

2 Stir in red curry paste and cook for a few more minutes.

3 Stir in the lime juice, fish sauce, capsicum and water; simmer for about 10 minutes.

4 Mix cooked arrowroot with water to make a paste; stir the paste into the sauce to thicken it.

5 Remove the pan from heat and add the toasted cashews to serve.

CHEF'S NOTE

A high protein diet is essential as it helps build and maintain muscle mass. Enjoy our protein rich pan-fried chilli beef that you can prepare ahead of time and carry to work as a cold lunch if you wish.

RED SNAPPER IN HOT VEGGIE SAUCE

30 DAY
FLAT BELLY SLIMDOWN

Ingredients

- 1kg/2¼ red snapper fillets
- 60ml/¼ cup extra virgin olive oil
- 1 green pepper, chopped
- 4 spring onions, thinly sliced
- 2 tomatoes, diced
- 2 cloves garlic

- 2 tbsp fresh lemon juice
- 120ml/½ cup freshly squeezed lime juice
- 1 tsp cayenne pepper
- 1 tsp pepper
- Fresh chopped coriander for garnish

Method

1 Add extra virgin olive oil to a frying pan and sauté the garlic gently for about 4 minutes or until golden brown.

2 Place the fish in the oil and drizzle with lemon and lime juice.

3 Sprinkle with black pepper and cayenne pepper and top with green peppers, spring onions, and tomatoes.

4 Cover the frying pan and gently cook for about 15 minutes or until the fish is cooked through and flakes easily with fork.

5 To serve, garnish with coriander.

CHEF'S NOTE

Nothing spells out healthy more than a serving of fish cooked in olive oil. Savour each bite of our nutrient rich low carb red snapper recipe.

SPICY ROAST CHICKEN

Ingredients

- 1 whole chicken
- 2 tbsp olive oil
- ½ tsp Spanish paprika
- ½ tsp salt
- ½ tsp crushed basil

- ½ tsp crushed oregano
- ¼ tsp cayenne pepper (or more if you like it spicy)
- ½ tsp ground black pepper
- 1 tsp all-spice

Method

1 Pre-heat your oven to 220°C/450°F/8 gas mark.

2 Remove any extra fat from the chicken.

3 Mix all the dry ingredients together.

4 In a baking pan, rub the chicken with olive oil and sprinkle the dry ingredients on the chicken.

5 Roast the chicken for 25 minutes and then reduce the heat to 180 degrees Fahrenheit and cook for 20 minutes per every lb of weight (or until the chicken is piping hot and cooked through to an internal temperature of 165 degrees Fahrenheit.

CHEF'S NOTE
Remove the chicken from the oven and let it cool for 10 minutes before serving with a mound of fresh vegetables. This is a healthy and easy to make recipe perfect for a weekend dinner with guests.

BAKED SALMON WITH HERBS & LEMON

30 DAY
FLAT BELLY SLIMDOWN

Ingredients

- 6 x 175g/6oz Atlantic salmon fillets, with skin on
- 120ml/½ cup extra virgin olive oil
- 1 bunch roughly chopped lemon thyme
- 75g/3oz finely chopped dill leaves

- 2 tbsp drained and chopped capers
- 2 fresh lemons, juiced
- 2 garlic cloves, finely chopped
- A pinch of sea salt

Method

1 In a large jug, mix together lemon thyme, dill, capers, vinegar, garlic, extra virgin olive oil, sea salt and pepper.

2 Arrange the salmon fillets, in a single layer, in a ceramic dish and pour over half of the marinade. Turn it over and pour over the remaining marinade.

3 Refrigerate, covered, for about 4 hours.

4 Remove the fish from the refrigerator at least 30 minutes before cooking.

5 Pre-heat your oven to 200°C/400°F/6 gas mark and cook the salmon for around 20 mins or until the salmon is cooked thorough.

CHEF'S NOTE

You can use any other white fish in place of salmon. Serve this salmon dish garnished with fresh lemon wedges.

TASTY SALMON WITH FENNEL & FRESH HERBS

SERVES 4

30 DAY
FLAT BELLY SLIMDOWN

Ingredients

- 500g/18oz wild salmon fillets
- A handful of fennel fronds
- 1 tbsp chopped parsley
- 1 tbsp chopped dill
- 1 tbsp chopped chives

- 1 tbsp chopped tarragon
- 1 tbsp chopped basil
- 1 tbsp extra-virgin olive oil
- 1 tbsp chopped shallot
- 1 tbsp lemon juice

Method

1 Lightly oil a steamer basket with olive oil.

2 Add the salmon and fennel wedges and steam for about 6-10 minutes or until the salmon is cooked through.

3 Meanwhile in a bowl, combine the chopped herbs, extra virgin olive oil, and shallot and lemon juice; stir until well combined.

4 Season and spoon over cooked fish.

CHEF'S NOTE
This steamed salmon served with fennel and fresh herbs is healthy with great depth of flavors.

INSTANT POT HEARTY TURKEY STEW

SERVES 4

30 DAY
FLAT BELLY SLIMDOWN

Ingredients

- 500g/1lb 2oz diced turkey
- 1 tbsp coconut oil
- 1 red onion, chopped
- 3 garlic cloves, minced
- 1 litre/4 cups water

- 1 tbsp curry powder
- 2½ tsp spice mix (cumin, turmeric, cinnamon, paprika, and red pepper)
- 60g/2 ½ oz parsley

Method

1 Set your instant pot on sauté mode and melt coconut oil; sauté onion and garlic until fragrant and then brown in turkey.

2 Add in the remaining ingredients and stir to mix well and lock lid.

3 Cook on high pressure for 15 minutes and then release pressure naturally.

4 Serve garnished with parsley.

CHEF'S NOTE

Healthy fats and protein are your secret weapon for weight loss. This quick cooking healthy dinner, combines the leanness of turkey with the savoury goodness of Thai spices to make an amazing dinner. Enjoy this hearty turkey stew that's delicious and super-healthy.

ORANGE & CRANBERRY CRUSTED SALMON

30 DAY
FLAT BELLY SLIMDOWN

Ingredients

- Olive oil cooking spray
- 4 x (100g/3 ½ oz each) salmon fillets
- Salt & pepper to taste
- 2 tbsp extra virgin olive oil
- 60g/2 ½ oz dried cranberries, chopped
- 125g/4oz walnuts, chopped
- 1 tsp orange zest
- 1 tbsp Dijon mustard
- 2 tbsp parsley, chopped

Method

1 Preheat your oven to 180°C/350°F/4 gas mark.

2 Lightly coat a baking tray with olive oil cooking spray.

3 Generously season the fish fillets with sea salt and pepper and arrange them on the baking tray.

4 Mix the remaining ingredients in a small bowl until well blended; press onto the fillets and bake in the preheated oven for about 20 minutes or until the fish is cooked through and the topping is lightly browned.

5 Remove from the oven and serve.

CHEF'S NOTE
Use chopped almonds or pecans instead of walnuts. You can also replace olive oil with sesame or coconut oil.

LEMONGRASS & CHILLI BEEF

SERVES 4

30 DAY

FLAT BELLY SLIMDOWN

Ingredients

- 100g/3 ½ oz courgette noodles
- 250g/9oz extra-lean beef steak, trimmed, sliced
- ½ tbsp sunflower oil
- 1 tsp fish sauce
- Juice of 1 lime

- 1 garlic clove
- ½ piece ginger, chopped
- 1 lemongrass stem, chopped
- 1 red chilli, chopped
- 125g/4oz each mint, basil and coriander
- 1 spring onion, sliced

Method

1 In a food processor, process together garlic, ginger, lemongrass and chilli into a paste.

2 Add a tbsp oil, fish sauce, and lime juice and process until well combined.

3 Toss meat in a large bowl with half marinade and chill for at least 15 minutes.

4 In the meantime, cook courgette noodles; drain and rinse under cold water.

5 Toss the noodles with the remaining marinade.

6 Add the oil to a pan set over a medium high heat; add the beef and cook for about 7 minutes or until browned.

7 Toss together with courgette noodles, herbs and onions in a bowl and serve.

CHEF'S NOTE
This healthy beef dish is the ultimate dinner hour comfort food especially in cold weather. It's low in cabs and very high in healthy fat and protein.

FRIED TILAPIA FILLETS

30 DAY
FLAT BELLY SLIMDOWN

Ingredients

- 500g/1lb 2oz tilapia fillets, skin and bones removed
- ¼ tsp basil
- ¼ tsp ground paprika
- ¼ tsp oregano
- ¼ tsp ground white pepper

- ¼ tsp thyme
- ¼ tsp ground black pepper
- 2 tsp salt
- ¼ tsp onion powder
- ¼ tsp ground cayenne pepper
- 2 tsp extra virgin olive oil

Method

1 Add oregano, basil, thyme, black pepper, white pepper, salt, onion powder, cayenne pepper, and paprika to a small bowl.

2 Mix the spices until well combined.

3 Brush fthe ish with half of oil and sprinkle with the spice mixture.

4 Drizzle with the remaining oil and cook fish in a frying pan set over high heat until blackened and flakes easily with a fork.

CHEF'S NOTE

Try combining chopped sundried tomatoes, parsley and fresh lemon zest with olive oil in a large bowl and quickly fry for a tasty side accompaniment

CHICKEN WITH PEPPERS

30 DAY
FLAT BELLY SLIMDOWN

Ingredients

- 2 tsp extra virgin olive oil
- 350g/12oz chicken breasts halved lengthways, skinless, boneless, trimmed
- 3 kalamata olives
- 2 large tomatoes, chopped
- 2 green peppers, cut into small strips

- 1 red onion, sliced
- Cooking oil spray
- 1 tsp oregano, chopped
- ½ tbsp parsley, chopped
- ¼ tsp pepper
- ¼ tsp salt

Method

1 In a nonstick frying pan, sauté onion in oil over medium high heat for about 5 minutes or until golden brown.

2 Raise the heat to high and stir in the green peppers; sauté until the peppers are tender.

3 Stir in tomato, black pepper & salt and continue cooking for 7 more minutes or until all liquid has evaporated.

4 Stir in the olives, oregano, and parsley and cook for a minute more.

5 Transfer the mixture to a bowl and keep warm.

6 Wipe the pan clean and coat it lightly with cooking spray.

7 Add chicken and cook until piping hot and cooked through.

8 Stir in the tomato mixture and cook until heated through, for about 1 minute.

CHEF'S NOTE

A high protein high fat diet is essential as it helps build and maintain muscle mass. Enjoy our low carb high fat high protein chicken dish that you can prepare ahead of time and carry to work as a cold lunch.

WARM LEMON CHICKEN

Ingredients

- 350g/12oz chicken thighs, skinless, boneless
- ½ red cabbage, shredded
- 2 handfuls baby spinach leaves
- 1 tsp balsamic vinegar

- 1 carrots, cut into ribbons
- ½ tsp extra virgin olive oil
- 1 sprig thyme
- Juice and zest from ½ lemon
- 1 crushed garlic cloves

Method

1 Remove the skin from the chicken and place it between two sheets of cling film; bash with a meat tenderizer or a rolling pin to flatten.

2 Place the chicken in a dish and generously season with pepper and salt.

3 Stir in half lemon juice and lemon zest and sprinkle with thyme.

4 Set a pan or griddle over medium heat and fry the chicken for about 15 minutes or until cooked through and golden brown.

5 In a bowl, combine the carrots, red cabbage and spinach. Divide between serving plates and top each with chicken.

6 Drizzle with the remaining lemon juice, balsamic vinegar and cooking juices to serve.

CHEF'S NOTE
You can add whichever vegetables you wish to this dish to bulk it up.

SLOW COOKER ITALIAN BEEF WITH AVOCADO

30 DAY
FLAT BELLY SLIMDOWN

Ingredients

- 1 kg/36oz grass-fed chuck roast
- 4 tbsp olive oil
- 3 cloves garlic
- 1 tsp marjoram
- 1 tsp basil
- 1 tsp oregano
- ½ tsp ground ginger
- 1 tsp onion powder
- 2 tsp garlic powder
- 1 tsp salt
- 60ml/¼ cup apple cider vinegar
- 250ml/1 cup water
- 250ml/1 cup coconut cream
- 2 avocados, sliced

Method

1 Cut slits in the roast with a sharp knife and then stuff with garlic cloves.

2 Preheat the slow cooker to a high setting.

3 In a bowl, whisk together marjoram, basil, oregano, ground ginger, onion powder, garlic powder, and salt until well blended; rub the seasoning all over the roast and place in the slow cooker.

4 Add the vinegar and water, cover and cook for 6-8 hours or until cooked through and tender.

5 When it's ready shred the meat with a fork; stir in coconut cream

6 Serve along with cooking juices topped with avocado.

CHEF'S NOTE
This dish is very low in carbs and high heart-healthy fat and protein.

GRILLED SALMON WITH TASTY MUSHROOMS

30 DAY
FLAT BELLY SLIMDOWN

Ingredients

- 4 x 100g/3½ oz each salmon fillets
- 250g/9oz sliced mushrooms, sliced
- 2 tbsp extra virgin olive oil
- ½ tbsp chopped fresh thyme leaves
- 2 tbsp minced shallots
- 1 tbsp minced garlic

- 1 tbsp freshly squeezed lemon juice
- 1 tsp Herbes de Provence
- A pinch of sea salt
- A pinch pepper
- Parsley sprigs and lemon wedges

Method

1 Preheat your grill to medium low.

2 Brush the fish fillets with 1 tsp of extra virgin olive oil and sprinkle with salt and pepper and grill for about 6 minutes per side or until cooked through.

3 In the meantime, set a sauté pan over high heat and add the remaining olive oil. Add the mushrooms, sea salt & black pepper and sauté for about a few minutes along with the garlic, shallots & thyme

4 Stir in Herbes de Provence and lemon juice; adjust salt and pepper.

5 Place the fish to a serving platter and top with the mushroom mixture; garnish with parsley and lemons to serve.

CHEF'S NOTE
Substitute Herbes de Provence with fresh herbs– a mix of fresh basil, parsley, and oregano would work perfectly. Best served with a glass of chilled fresh orange juice.

ASIAN STYLE CURRIED PRAWNS

30 DAY
FLAT BELLY SLIMDOWN

Ingredients

- 250g/9oz prawns
- 4 fresh tomatoes, pureed
- 1 medium finely chopped onion
- 2 garlic cloves, minced
- 4 tbsp extra virgin olive oil

- ½ tsp turmeric
- ½ tsp coriander
- ½ tsp cumin
- 2 tsp fresh ginger, minced

Method

1 Heat oil in a saucepan set over medium heat; sauté onion and garlic until tender.

2 Stir in tomatoes and spices and cook for about 5 minutes.

3 Add prawns to the simmering mixture and cook for about 10 minutes or until cooked through.

4 Remove the pan from heat and drizzle with lime juice.

CHEF'S NOTE
Serve this prawn dish hot drizzled with two tbsp of freshly squeezed lemon or lime juice.

SPICY GRILLED COD

30 DAY
FLAT BELLY SLIMDOWN

Ingredients

- 500g/1lb 2oz cod fillets
- 2 tbsp extra-virgin olive oil
- 2 minced garlic cloves
- ⅛ tsp cayenne pepper
- 3 tbsp fresh lime juice

- 1½ tsp fresh lemon juice
- 60g/¼ cup freshly squeezed orange juice
- 80ml/1/3 cup water
- 1 tbsp chopped fresh thyme
- 2 tbsp chopped fresh chives

Method

1 In a bowl, mix together the lemon, lime juice, orange, cayenne pepper, extra virgin olive oil, garlic and water.

2 Place the fish in a dish and add the marinade, reserving 60ml/¼ cup; marinate in the refrigerator for at least 30 minutes.

3 Grill the marinated fish for about 4 minutes per side, basting regularly with the marinade.

4 Serve the grilled fish on a plate and top with the reserved marinade, thyme and chives.

CHEF'S NOTE

Cod is super endowed with omega-2 fatty acids and thyme and spring onions add a healthy dose of vitamins, fibre and carotenoids. Enjoy every single bite of this simple but nutritious dinner.

HEALTHY TURKEY WITH CITRUS AVOCADO RELISH

30 DAY
FLAT BELLY SLIMDOWN

Ingredients

For the avocado relish:
- ½ avocado, diced
- 1 seedless orange, cut into segments and discarding the membranes
- 1 small onion, finely chopped
- 1 tsp apple cider vinegar
- 1 tbsp fresh coriander, chopped

For the turkey
- ½ tsp 5-spice powder
- 2 tbsp extra virgin olive oil
- 1 tbsp chilli powder
- A good pinch of salt
- 225g/8oz turkey cutlets
- 250ml/1 cup chicken broth

Method

1 Combine the avocado, orange segments, onion, vinegar and coriander and toss well.

2 Next, combine all the spices for the turkey in a shallow bowl then cover the cutlets in the spice mix.

3 Add the oil to your frying pan set over medium heat and sear the turkey until cooked and tender for about 3-5 minutes on each side.

4 Add 250ml/1 cup of chicken broth and simmer for about 10 minutes.

5 take the cutlets out of the liquid, plate up and serve with the avocado relish.

CHEF'S NOTE
Cutlets are boneless cuts of meat which have been pounded thin - you can do this yourself with turkey breasts.

30 DAY

DAY

FLAT BELLY SLIMDOWN

SNACK
RECIPES

SERVES 2

CRISPY LEMON CHILLI ROASTED KALE

Ingredients

- 2 bunches kale, ribs and stems removed, roughly chopped
- 2 tbsp lemon juice
- 2 tbsp extra-virgin olive oil
- 1 tsp lemon salt
- 2 tsp chilli powder

Method

1 Preheat oven to 140°C /275°F/1 gas mark.

2 In a large bowl, massage together the kale, lemon juice, extra virgin olive oil, lemon salt and chilli powder until kale is tender.

3 Spread the kale on a baking tray and bake for about 20 minutes or until crisp.

4 Remove from oven and serve warm.

CHEF'S NOTE
You could use freshly squeezed lime juice instead of lemon juice. Add a pinch of cayenne for spicier kale crisps.

SWEET POTATO CRUNCHES

30 DAY

FLAT BELLY SLIMDOWN

Ingredients

- 1 sweet potato, peeled and cut into thin julienne strips
- 1 tbsp extra-virgin olive oil
- Pinch of cayenne pepper
- Pinch of cinnamon

Method

1 Preheat oven to 180°C/350°F/4 gas mark.

2 Add the potato strips into a large bowl and drizzle with extra virgin olive oil and sprinkle with cayenne pepper and cinnamon.

3 Toss to coat well and then spread evenly onto a baking tray.

4 Bake for about 30 minutes, stirring every 10 minutes, until crispy.

CHEF'S NOTE

This recipe is sure to become one of your favourite and go-to options whenever you want to snack on something healthy. Eat as a snack, salad topper or atop soup and many other side dishes.

GRILLED COURGETTE WITH A TWIST

SERVES 2

30 DAY
FLAT BELLY SLIMDOWN

Ingredients

- 2 tsp olive oil
- 2 large courgettes, sliced lengthways in 3 slices
- 3 tbsp balsamic vinegar

- ¾ tsp garlic powder
- ¼ tsp salt
- 1 tsp all-spice

Method

1 Pre-heat the oven at 140°C/275°F/1 gas mark.

2 Sprinkle or brush the courgettes with olive oil then sprinkle all the dry ingredients.

3 Place the courgettes in the oven and bake for 3 minutes on each side.

4 Brush the balsamic vinegar on both sides and continue baking for 1 minute each side or until the courgettes are tender.

CHEF'S NOTE

This is an awesome and healthy snack made with fresh courgettes and heart-healthy olive oil.

CURRIED CASHEWS

Ingredients

- 500g/18oz roasted cashews
- 2 tbsp ghee
- ¼ tsp cayenne
- 4 tsp mild curry powder
- 1 tsp sea salt

Method

1 Preheat oven to 180°C/350°F/4 gas mark.

2 In a small frying pan set over medium heat, melt the ghee and then add cayenne pepper, curry powder and salt.

3 Cook for about 30 seconds or until fragrant.

4 In a baking tray, toss together the curry butter and cashews until well coated and then spread the cashews in a single layer.

5 Bake for about 10 minutes or until hot and shiny. Cool to room temperature before serving.

CHEF'S NOTE
These curried cashews are spicy and very tasty. Cashew nuts are a great source of omega 3 fatty acids.

CARROT FRENCH CHIPS

SERVES 2

Ingredients

- 2 tbsp extra virgin olive oil
- 6 large carrots
- ½ tsp sea salt

Method

1 Chop the carrots into 2-inch sections and then cut each section into thin sticks.

2 Toss together the carrots sticks with extra virgin olive oil and salt in a bowl.

3 Spread into a baking tray lined with parchment paper.

4 Bake the carrot sticks at 425°F for about 20 minutes or until browned.

CHEF'S NOTE

This is a low calorie healthy snack made with healthy ingredients. Olive oil is a heart-healthy fat while carrots are rich in carotenes – antioxidants that help prevent cardiovascular disease and eye problems and keeps the skin young and lungs healthy.

SERVES 12

SESAME CRACKERS

30 DAY

FLAT BELLY SLIMDOWN

Ingredients

- 250g/9oz sesame seeds
- 2 tbsp grapeseed oil
- 2 large free range eggs, beaten

- 1 ½ tsp sea salt
- 750g/27oz almond flour, blanched

Method

1 Stir together sesame seeds, almond flour, oil, eggs and salt in a large bowl until well combined and formed into a dough

2 Divide the dough into two portions.

3 Place each into two baking trays lined with parchment papers and cover with parchment paper.

4 Spread the dough between the papers to cover the entire baking tray and remove the top paper.

5 With a pizza cutter or knife, cut the dough into 2-inch squares and bake at 350°F until golden brown, for about 12 minutes.

6 Cool before serving.

CHEF'S NOTE

Sesame seeds an excellent source of copper, calcium, magnesium, iron, phosphorus, vitamin B1, zinc, molybdenum, selenium, and dietary fibre.

HEALTHY SPICED NUTS

Ingredients

- 1 tbsp extra virgin olive oil
- 60g/2 ½ oz walnuts
- 60g/2 ½ oz pecans
- 60g/2 ½ oz almonds

- ½ tsp sea salt
- ½ tsp pepper
- ½ tsp cumin
- 1 tsp chilli powder

Method

1 Put the nuts in a frying pan set over medium heat and toast until lightly browned.

2 In the meantime, prepare the spice mixture; combine black pepper, cumin, chilli and salt in a bowl.

3 Coat the toasted nuts with extra virgin olive oil and sprinkle with the spice mixture.

4 Serve right away.

CHEF'S NOTE
Chop the nuts into halves to create more of an even surface area for a larger spice coating to nut ratio. These nuts can also be added to a salad for an extra bit of crunchiness.

SERVES 2

SESAME CARROTS

30 DAY
FLAT BELLY SLIMDOWN

Ingredients

- 500g/18oz baby carrots, sliced lengthways
- 1 tbsp toasted sesame seeds
- Pinch of kosher salt
- Pinch of dried thyme

Method

1 Add carrots in a small bowl.

2 Add in sesame seeds, salt and thyme.

3 Toss until well combined.

4 Serve right away.

CHEF'S NOTE

This is a nutrient-dense recipe made with healthy ingredients. Sesame seeds are nutritious rich in calcium, copper, magnesium and vitamins that help in boosting our immune system.

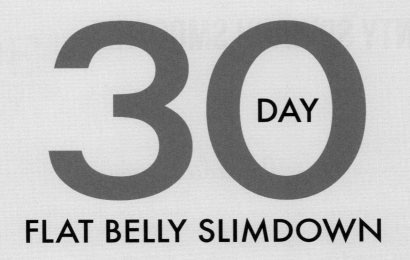

30 DAY

FLAT BELLY SLIMDOWN

SMOOTHIE
RECIPES

MINTY SPINACH SMOOTHIE

SERVES 2

30 DAY
FLAT BELLY SLIMDOWN

Ingredients

- 60g/2½ oz fresh mint leaves, roughly chopped
- 375g/13oz fresh spinach, roughly chopped
- 250g/9oz chopped kale
- 375ml/1½ cups chilled water
- 1 cucumber
- 250g/9oz frozen pineapple chunks
- ½ an avocado, chopped

Method

1 Add the mint, spinach and water to a blender.

2 Blend until very smooth.

3 Add the remaining ingredients to the blender and continue blending until very smooth.

4 Serve right away.

CHEF'S NOTE

The veggies and fruits in this smoothie will help the body purge the excess fat and improve your health in general. Avocado is rich in folic acid, vitamins B, C and E, fibre, magnesium, and potassium –all of which are play a vital role in burning fat and keeping your body healthy.

WINTER GREENS SMOOTHIE

Ingredients

- 250g/9oz chopped kale with the stems and ribs removed
- 3 broccoli florets, roughly chopped and frozen
- 250g/9oz chopped spinach
- 1 apple, chopped

- 125ml/½ cup freshly squeezed orange juice
- 60ml/¼ cup fresh carrot juice
- 1 banana, chopped and frozen
- 1 tsp spirulina
- 1 tsp chia seeds

Method

1 Combine the kale, broccoli spinach, carrot juice and orange juice in your blender.

2 Pulse until smooth.

3 Add in the remaining smoothie ingredients and blend to desired consistency.

4 Serve immediately.

CHEF'S NOTE

This smoothie is choc full of health-giving nutrients, fibre, healthy omega fats, vitamins and minerals. Spinach is an excellent antioxidant and a rich source of vitamin K; broccoli is low in calories and packed with a huge range of nutrients such as vitamin C, K and calcium.

VITAMIN C RICH GREEN SMOOTHIE

30 DAY
FLAT BELLY SLIMDOWN

Ingredients

- 2 kiwi fruits, peeled & chopped
- 2 tbsp chopped coriander
- 250g/9oz chopped kale leaves
- 1 celery rib, chopped

- 120ml/½ cup freshly squeezed tangerine or orange juice
- 60g/2 ½ oz crushed ice

Method

1 Combine the kale, coriander, and celery and tangerine/orange juice in a blender.

2 Blend until smooth.

3 Add in the kiwi and crushed ice and continue blending until completely smooth.

4 Serve in a tall glass.

CHEF'S NOTE
Rich in vitamin C, this smoothie is super-healthy and very tasty. Coriander is excellent for the digestive system and nervous system; it's rich in iron and great for the skin.

APPLE CABBAGE SMOOTHIE

30 DAY
FLAT BELLY SLIMDOWN

Ingredients

- 2-3 celery stalks
- ½ medium red cabbage
- 1 tbsp freshly squeezed lemon juice
- 2 red apples, chopped

Method

1 Combine the celery and cabbage in a juicer.

2 Next pour the juice in a blender.

3 Add in the lemon juice and apples and blend until smooth.

4 Chill in the fridge and serve cold.

CHEF'S NOTE

This smoothie is made with amazing hormone-balancing ingredients. Cabbage is rich in vitamin C and vitamin K. It's low in calories and low on the Glycemic Index. Apples are among the best fruits rich in nutrients. They are rich in plant compounds that keep the heart healthy, vitamin C to improve brain function and are a good natural source of potassium to help prevent fluid retention.

BANANA PLUM SMOOTHIE

Ingredients

- 4 plums, pitted then chopped
- 1 banana
- 180ml/¾ cup almond milk

- 1 tbsp chia seeds
- ½ tbsp coconut oil

Method

1 Combine all ingredients in your blender or food processor.

2 Pulse until smooth.

3 Serve chilled in a tall glass.

4 Enjoy!

CHEF'S NOTE

This smoothie features coconut oil, which plays a big role in boosting hormone health. It helps with the production of hormones, reduces inflammation, and has antibacterial and antimicrobial properties. Chia seeds and almond milk are also great hormone-balancing foods. Coconut oil is an excellent healthy fat that helps with so many things, but in particular lowers cholesterol, supports the immune system; gives you energy; reduces heart disease; helps with menopause pain and cramps; helps you sleep better and more.

BEETROOT & GRAPE SMOOTHIE

30 DAY
FLAT BELLY SLIMDOWN

Ingredients

- 1 banana
- 1 bunch seedless grapes
- 1 beetroot, washed, peeled and chopped
- 4 baby carrots
- 2 small slices pineapple

- 1 tbsp chia seeds
- 2 tsp coconut oil
- 60ml/¼ cup coconut water
- Mint leaves for garnishing

Method

1 Combine all the smoothie ingredients in your blender or food processor.

2 Pulse until creamy and smooth.

3 Serve in a tall glass and garnish with mint leaves.

4 Enjoy!

CHEF'S NOTE

Loaded with healthy superfoods such as chia seeds and coconut oil, this smoothie is great for hormone health. Coconut oil is an excellent healthy fat that helps so many things, but in particular lowers cholesterol, supports the immune system; gives you energy; reduces heart disease; helps with menopause pain and cramps;

POMEGRANATE BLUEBERRY SMOOTHIE

30 DAY
FLAT BELLY SLIMDOWN

Ingredients

- 3 tbsp pomegranate seeds
- 2 apples, chopped
- 250g/1 cup blueberries
- 1 banana, chopped

- 1 tbsp coconut oil
- ½ chopped avocado
- 120ml/½ cup coconut water

Method

1 Add the pomegranate arils (the seeds) and the apples to a juicer.

2 Process them together to make the juice.

3 Combine this juice with the remaining ingredients in your blender.

4 Pulse until smooth.

5 Enjoy!

CHEF'S NOTE

With nutrient-rich ingredients such as blueberries, apples, avocado, pomegranates, coconut oil and coconut water, this smoothie is super healthy. Avocado contains vitamin E, which helps with hot flushes, boosts the immune system and helps keeping skin healthy. It's also an excellent source of monounsaturated fat to help lower cholesterol. Avocado is also rich in magnesium and vitamin K to keep bones healthy.

ANTIOXIDANT RICH BERRY SMOOTHIE

30 DAY
FLAT BELLY SLIMDOWN

Ingredients

- 250g/9oz raspberries
- 250g/9oz strawberries
- 1 banana
- 1 tbsp goji berry powder

- 1 tbsp flax meal
- 1 scoop vanilla protein powder
- 250ml/1 cup almond milk, unsweetened

Method

1 Add all smoothie ingredients to your blender or food processor.

2 Pulse until super smooth.

3 Refrigerate for at least one hour.

4 Serve in a tall glass.

5 Enjoy!

CHEF'S NOTE

Flax meal is one of the most powerful superfoods found in nature. It's packed with phytoestrogen compounds that help protect the body against many types of cancer, such as breast, colon and prostate.

STRAWBERRY COCONUT WATER SMOOTHIE

30 DAY
FLAT BELLY SLIMDOWN

Ingredients

- 125g/4oz strawberries
- 125g/4oz cherries
- 1 banana, chopped
- 250ml/1 cup unsweetened coconut water, chilled

- 1 tsp green tea powder
- 1 scoop protein powder
- 1 tbsp chia seed powder
- 1 tbsp coconut oil

Method

1 Mix all the ingredients in your blender or food processor.

2 Process until very smooth.

3 Refrigerate for about 30 minutes before serving.

4 Serve in a tall glass and enjoy!

CHEF'S NOTE

Strawberries are an excellent source of vitamins C and K as well as providing a good dose of fibre, folic acid, manganese and potassium.

STRAWBERRY FLAX MEAL SMOOTHIE

30 DAY
FLAT BELLY SLIMDOWN

Ingredients

- 125g/4oz strawberries, sliced
- 1 banana
- 2 tsp flax meal
- 250ml/1 cup fresh red grape juice
- 1 scoop vanilla protein powder
- Handful of crushed ice
- 1 tsp maca powder

Method

1 Combine all the ingredients in a blender.

2 Process until extra smooth.

3 Refrigerate your smoothie for about 30 minutes or until chilled to your liking.

4 Serve.

CHEF'S NOTE

This is a very nutritious and delicious smoothie recipe. Maca is rich in essential minerals, especially selenium, calcium, magnesium and iron – all of which have important functions in keeping your system healthy.

GINGER INFUSED CANTALOUPE SMOOTHIE

SERVES 1

30 DAY
FLAT BELLY SLIMDOWN

Ingredients

- ½ a cantaloupe melon, cut in cubes
- ½ tsp freshly grated ginger root
- 180ml/¾ cup coconut milk
- 250g/9oz ice cubes

Method

1 Combine the melon, ginger, milk, and ice cubes in your blender.

2 Pulse until smooth or desired consistency is achieved.

3 Chill for at least 30 minutes before serving.

4 Enjoy!

CHEF'S NOTE

This ginger-infused smoothie is loaded with health-giving ingredients that will not only leave you full but also healthy. Cantaloupe scores "excellent" in its many health benefits including lowering the risk of metabolic syndrome and inflammation; it's a rich source of vitamin A, which play an important role in the production of sebum. Just like coconut water, coconut milk is very nutritious and rich in fibre, calcium, magnesium, phosphorus, iron and selenium, and vitamins Bs, C and E.

SERVES 1

TROPICAL FRUIT SMOOTHIE WITH CARROTS

30 DAY
FLAT BELLY SLIMDOWN

Ingredients

- 60ml/¼ cup unsweetened coconut water
- 125g/4oz frozen pineapple chunks
- ½ banana, sliced
- 125g/4oz frozen mango chunks
- 75g/3oz grated carrots
- 125ml/½ cup coconut milk
- 1 scoop protein powder
- 1 tsp maca powder
- 1 tsp spirulina
- 1 tbsp toasted sesame seeds
- 1 tsp coconut oil

Method

1 Combine all the tropical smoothie ingredients into your blender.

2 Pulse until smooth.

3 Serve in a tall glass and enjoy.

CHEF'S NOTE

This is a super healthy smoothie, loaded with all good things for a great health – superfoods, fibres, essential fatty acids, and saturated fats. Carrots are rich in carotenes – antioxidants that help us from cardiovascular disease and eye problems and keeps the skin young and lungs healthy.

MIXED FRUIT COCONUT WATER SMOOTHIE

30 DAY
FLAT BELLY SLIMDOWN

Ingredients

- 250g/9oz frozen strawberries
- 250g/9oz frozen mango chunks
- 250g/9oz chopped baby carrots
- 1 navel orange, peeled and segmented
- 250ml/1 cup unsweetened coconut water, semi-frozen
- 250g/9oz toasted sunflower seeds

Method

1 Combine all the smoothie ingredients in your blender.

2 Blend for about 30 seconds or until very smooth.

3 Chill for 1 hour.

4 Serve into two tall glasses.

CHEF'S NOTE

With coconut water, fruits and veggies, this smoothie is the best. Oranges are excellent source of vitamin C, which protects against cell damage that can cause ageing and disease. Sunflower seeds are rich in vitamin E, which has special benefits during and after menopause. Helps slow down the signs of ageing – protecting us from heart disease and arthritis.

SERVES 1

MANGO SUPERFOOD SMOOTHIE

30 DAY
FLAT BELLY SLIMDOWN

Ingredients

- 60g/2½ oz frozen mango chunks
- 1 chopped banana, frozen
- 1 tbsp natural almond butter
- 120ml/½ cup almond milk, unsweetened

- 1 tsp spirulina
- 1 tsp chia seeds
- 1 tsp goji berries

Method

1 Add all the ingredients to your blender or food processor.

2 Process until very until smooth.

3 Refrigerate until chilled.

4 Enjoy!

CHEF'S NOTE

Filled with superfoods, this smoothie is super healthy and very tasty. Spirulina is one of the most powerful hormone-balancing superfoods. Spinach is an excellent antioxidant and a great source of vitamin K.

SERVES 2

BEAUTY RELOADED SMOOTHIE

Ingredients

- 125g/4oz frozen blueberries
- 60g/2½ oz frozen strawberries
- 1 banana, chopped
- 1 orange, peeled and the pits removed
- 120ml/½ cup almond milk
- 2 tbsp chia seeds
- 125g/4oz toasted walnuts

Method

1 Combine all the ingredients in a power blender or food processor.

2 Process until super smooth.

3 Serve chilled.

4 Enjoy!

CHEF'S NOTE

This fruit and veggie loaded smoothie is an excellent hormone balancing treat. Walnuts are rich in omega-3 fats and antioxidants for health protection; almond milk is also a great hormone balancing food and oranges are excellent source of vitamin C, which protects against cell damage that can cause ageing and disease.